SWEDEN – JUST AMAZING!

Putting ideas
and innovations on the map

Anita Shenoi

ANITA SHENOI

Sweden
Just amazing!

PUTTING IDEAS AND
INNOVATIONS ON THE MAP

Published by
Kakao förlag
PO Box 1505
22101 Lund
Sweden
www.kakao.se

Text: Anita Shenoi
Printing: DZS Grafik, Slovenia
via Italgraf Media, 2015
ISBN 9789187795022

CONTENTS

Sweden

Location: Northern Europe, bordering the Baltic Sea, Gulf of Bothnia, Kattegat, and Skagerrak, between Finland and Norway

Geographic coordinates: 62 00 N, 15 00 E

Total area: 449,964 km²

Total length: 1,574 km

Population: 9.7 million

Unique Selling Point: an incubator of innovation through every era

13

Sweden
Just amazing!

PUTTING IDEAS AND INNOVATIONS ON THE MAP

For a small country, Sweden has a remarkable track record of delivering ideas and innovations with global impact. From dam-busting dynamite and the humble home refrigerator to Skype and Spotify, Swedish inventions have been changing the way we live, decade after decade. And while just over one hundred years ago, Sweden was one of the poorest countries in Europe, it is now the leader of innovation among EU member states.

So how did Sweden get to be so amazing? And will it continue its winning streak?

Why not join me on this regional tour of the country to investigate the past, present and future, the brilliant and the downright quirky, and see for yourself how Sweden keeps putting ideas and innovations on the map!

Anita Shenoi

South Sweden

HI-TECH HUB, GATEWAY TO THE CONTINENT

Cutesy cobbled streets, historic houses and atmospheric coastal vistas may all be part of the South Sweden experience – and the preferred settings for the trendiest Nordic Noir right now – but this region has seen phenomenal growth as a hi-tech hub, not least as a result of its glamorous new links with mainland Europe via the Öresund bridge.

Having prised itself out of the economic gloom following the end of the heavy-industrial era, Skåne (and particularly Malmö) has benefited from initiatives to boost local activity and innovation – so much so that the region is aiming to be the most innovative in Europe by 2020.

How has it done so far?

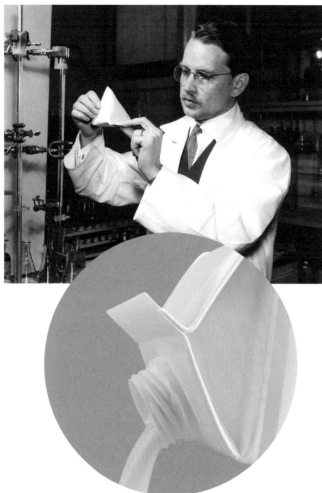

BOXING CLEVER

Eliminating the need for heavy glass bottles, Tetra Pak completely revolutionised grocery distribution in the 1950s with its aseptic, polyethylene-coated paper packages for liquids such as milk, cream and juice. Sixty years on from its conception in Lund, Tetra Pak is now a global leader in grocery packaging, its production exceeding 129 billion units in 2006, with 23 billion of these produced in China alone. The company's environmental ethos has also been recognised with the Swedish Forest Industries Federation Climate Award in 2010.

Above left: The historic heart of Lund

Above right: The revolutionary Tetrapak pyramid in the making

17

OUT OF THE BLUE

Inspired by the unitive powers of 10th Century Scandinavian king, Harald 'Blåtand', Lund-based Ericsson launched Bluetooth in 1998 and succeeded in uniting global tech businesses with an industry standard for wireless technology. Two years later, the first mobile phone with inbuilt Bluetooth was launched, and now more than three billion electronic gadgets from printers to digital cameras benefit from its connective brilliance.

SWEET LIKE CHOCOLATE

Succumbing to your sweet tooth on Facebook? You are not alone. More than 93 million people juggle jelly beans and flip fruity fish every day on their phones and tablets while playing Candy Crush Saga – the highly addictive game that synchronises seamlessly across social media platforms and devices, meaning players can pick up where they left off anytime, anywhere.
King's first games studio opened in Malmö in 2011 and new ones in London, Barcelona and Berlin have recently followed. The Malmö studio is also the brains behind Pet Rescue Saga – another smash hit game, with 15 million players daily.

The Hövding cycle helmet
before and after inflation

Left: The Bluetooth logo is composed of
Harald Bluetooth's runic initials

Left main picture: Malmö old town

HEAD-BANGING SOPHISTICATION

Malmö entrepreneurs Anna Haupt and Terese Alstin
came up with the idea for their air-bag style cycle helmet in 2005 while they were students. After winning the
Swedish Venture Cup in 2006 and a number of other
awards since then, the design duo have made their super
cool safety innovation a full-time business, with Hövding
Sweden AB selling the product worldwide.

Blekinge archipelago

Kullaberg nature reserve in Höganäs municipality. The area has been designated an Important Bird Area in Sweden

KEEPING AN EYE ON THE WORLD

Fancy a gigantic microscope in your backyard? Skåne has embraced the idea and won the localisation fight to build the European Spallation Source (ESS), a huge multidisciplinary research facility based on the world's most powerful neutron source. More than 17 countries are collaborating on the build, which is estimated to cost around EUR 1.84 billion.

Along with companion facility MAX IV, ESS will open up new possibilities for advanced research in fields such as health, the environment, energy, pharmaceuticals and archaeology. Work has already started on the site just outside of Lund, with MAX IV expected to be completed in 2016 and ESS in 2019.

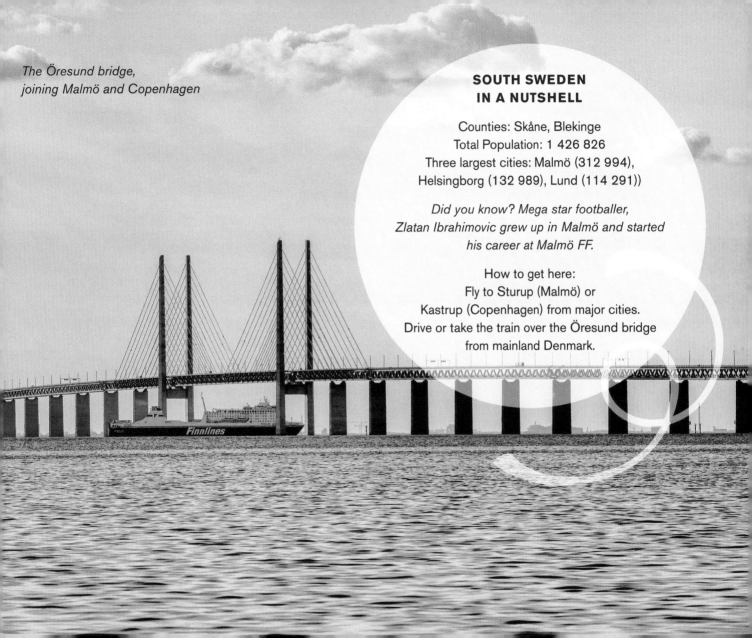

*The Öresund bridge,
joining Malmö and Copenhagen*

SOUTH SWEDEN
IN A NUTSHELL

Counties: Skåne, Blekinge
Total Population: 1 426 826
Three largest cities: Malmö (312 994),
Helsingborg (132 989), Lund (114 291))

*Did you know? Mega star footballer,
Zlatan Ibrahimovic grew up in Malmö and started
his career at Malmö FF.*

How to get here:
Fly to Sturup (Malmö) or
Kastrup (Copenhagen) from major cities.
Drive or take the train over the Öresund bridge
from mainland Denmark.

Västra Hamnen, Malmö.
Once an industrial eyesore,
now a popular residential area

The verdant pastures of Revinge hed

West Sweden

MECHANICAL GENIUS, SEAFOOD HEAVEN

Picture a herring jumping through a tyre and you might have a suitable redesign for Gothenburg's coat of arms – fishing and the automotive industry being the two mainstays of the region. And these are enduring motifs, as the west-coast capital's foodie reputation soars to Michelin heights while Volvo continues to impress with award-winning safety innovation.

Indeed, 'enduring innovation' may be a good descriptor for this part of Sweden, which has a long-standing reputation for technical excellence and demonstrates the ability to re-invent itself as changing times dictate. How so?

CRADLE OF CREATIVITY

As the ice receded and the vast granite rock faces here became exposed to the Bronze Age, early artistic types were inspired to make their mark on this canvas. But these were no rudimentary scratchings. In comparison with rock carvings in other parts of Scandinavia and the rest of the world, the etchings at Tanum (134 km north of Gothenburg) are outstanding in their artistic quality, variety and complexity, giving rich insights into the life and beliefs of the people who lived there around 1800-500 BC. There are more than 1,500 rock carving sites in the Tanum area, which was recognised by UNESCO as a World Heritage site in 1994.

FROM BALL-BEARINGS TO BIG TRUCKS

True to their name, Volvo have kept rolling – from their humble beginnings in 1915 as a subsidiary of SKF ball bearings, to the global vehicle, construction and engine manufacturer they are today, one hundred years on. As the age of the automobile progressed, Volvo cars and trucks built a lasting reputation for durability and safety, with ground-breaking innovations. A few highlights:

1959 The modern three-point safety belt

Volvo engineer Nils Bohlin is the man the world has to thank for dramatically reducing the number of fatal injuries in automobile accidents. The development of his seat belt and Volvo Cars waiving its patent rights for the benefit of everyone has saved an estimated million lives since then.

1976 Lambda Sond

Giving them the highest eco-credentials of the era, Volvo's world-first catalytic exhaust emission control with the Lambda Sond reduced pollutant discharge by some 90%. Today, virtually every petrol-driven car in the world is fitted with a Lambda Sond.

2002-2013

Roll-over protection system (ROPS), city safety (collision avoidance), and pedestrian and cyclist detection technology are some of Volvo's latest safety revolutions.

The early days of SKF

The elegant VOLVO PV445 DUETT was introduced in 1953 and is the ancestor of today's popular Volvo estate cars

Nils Bohlin

Right: The big wheel at Liseberg Amusement Park opened in 1967. Standing 30 metres tall and with a diameter of 25 metres, it was considered the largest modern Ferris wheel in the world at the time

Yeast cell experimentation at Sahlgrenska Academy

Acosense in action

A WOMB OF INVENTION

The days of inventors toiling away in obscurity are well and truly over as Swedish innovators are increasingly winning awards and receiving international attention. West Sweden is fortunate in having both the famous Sahlgrenska Academy and Chalmers university at the cutting edge of medical and technological innovation. Here is just a sample of their most up-to-date achievements and a glimpse of things to come...

Sahlgrenska

In September 2014 The world's first child was born after uterus transplantation from a live donor – the result of fifteen years of ground-breaking research helping women without wombs to give birth to their own children.

Looking forward

We may find out if there is a difference between how the female and male brain controls appetite. Young Gothenburg researcher Karolina Skibika was awarded a five-year SEK 8 million grant for her research on the role oestrogen plays in causing obesity.

Chalmers

In 2012 Linnéa Lindau became Sweden's inventor of the year after winning the Skapa prize of SEK 300 000 for an innovative method of analysing flowing liquids in pipes without having to take samples. Her business start-up Acosense is now literally flush with success.

Looking forward

Electricity generated from ocean waves may soon be coming your way if Sara West and Alexander Torstenfelt's Wavetube concept takes off. Having won the EU CleanLaunchPad competition in 2014, the duo have already secured soft funding from Sweden's Innovation Agency, Vinnova.

Right: Gothenburg is famous for its tram network

Käringön, one of the most westerly populated islands in Sweden, 2 km off the Bohuslän coast

The green tranquility of Halland

A TOOTHY TALE OF PEARLY WHITES

By remarkable coincidence, West Sweden can be credited with nurturing two of the most inventive minds in modern dental care:

Originally from a Halmstad farming family, Yngve Ericsson became Sweden's youngest dentist when he graduated at the age of 21 in 1933. Tooth decay and poor dental health was widespread in Sweden at this time, and Ericsson was kept busy. By 1949, he had written a doctoral thesis establishing the link between caries and enamel erosion, also stating the protective effects of fluoride. Although the benefit of fluoridated drinking water was already known in the US, there were problems with this and other systems of fluoride delivery. It was only when Yngve Ericsson developed one of the first truly effective fluoride toothpastes in the late 1950s that people had a convenient and effective means of caring for their teeth.

In 2011, Sahlgrenska odontologist Per-Ingvar Brånemark won the European Inventor Award Lifetime achievement category for developing osseointegration. In the 1950s, Brånemark discovered that titanium is not rejected by the body, and instead integrates with surrounding bone tissue. In 1965 he performed his first successful dental implant on a human subject and since then his methods have been refined to include other applications such as leg, arm and maxillofacial prostheses, improving the lives of millions who have suffered losses in these respects.

Did you know? The Swedish tradition of only allowing children to eat sweets on Saturdays originated in the 1950s, along with other efforts to improve the nation's dental health.

WEST SWEDEN IN A NUTSHELL

Counties: Västra Götaland, Halland
Total Population: 1 921 924
Three largest cities: Gothenburg (533 271)
Borås (105 995) Halmstad (94 084)

*Did you know? There's water, water, everywhere.
In addition to its miles of coastline,
Västra Götaland embraces both Lake Vättern
and Lake Vänern, the latter being the largest lake
in Sweden and the largest in the EU.*

*How to get here: Fly to Landvetter (Gothenburg)
from major international cities or why not try the
daily ferries from Kiel, Germany
or Fredrikshavn, Denmark?*

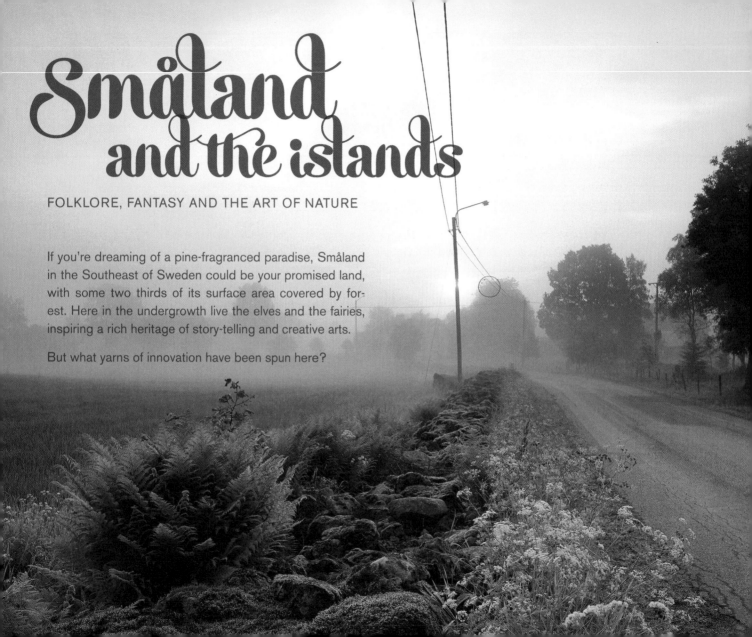

Småland
and the islands

FOLKLORE, FANTASY AND THE ART OF NATURE

If you're dreaming of a pine-fragranced paradise, Småland in the Southeast of Sweden could be your promised land, with some two thirds of its surface area covered by forest. Here in the undergrowth live the elves and the fairies, inspiring a rich heritage of story-telling and creative arts.

But what yarns of innovation have been spun here?

The inside workings of IKEA. The world's first IKEA store opened in Älmhult in 1953

IN THE BEGINNING THERE WAS ÄLMHULT

This tiny, rural municipality is famous for the genesis of systems-oriented genius not once but twice in its history, as the birth place of both 18th Century botanist, Carl Von Linné and 20th Century flat-pack king, Ingvar Kamprad. While Linné wowed the Scientific community of his time with Systema Naturae and set the standard for the way we classify the natural world today, Kamprad's IKEA has revolutionised home-furnishing habits and set the standard for modern design accessible to all.

Carl Von Linné and the linnea flower named after him

IT'S CRYSTAL CLEAR

A geographical cluster of fifteen glassworks in the area between Växjo and Kalmar, Glasriket (The Kingdom of Crystal) has been producing hand-blown glassware since 1742. Generations of Swedes and international visitors have delighted in the craftsmanship exhibited here, but traditional techniques have also left their mark on the environment – something the Kingdom of Crystal is now addressing. Coordinated by glass research institute Glafo, a three-year project is underway to devise techniques for removing lead and other poisons from old glass waste deposits, recycling the purified glass and re-using it. If successful, the project will kick-start clean-up initiatives nationwide and hopefully export its expertise to Europe, where lead glass is still produced.

Above: World renowned Kosta Boda glass design

CAPTIVATING TALES WITH TIMELESS CHARM

Ask ten Northern Europeans to describe Santa Claus or Pippi Longstocking and chances are that eight will all have the same images in mind – thanks to the female creators behind two of Sweden's most iconic cultural exports of the 20th Century. No doubt inspired by their picturesque surroundings and vivid imaginations, Jenny Nyström and Astrid Lindgren both embarked upon their creative journeys in Småland, the former conjuring up Scandinavia's favourite version of Santa and the latter becoming the third most translated children's book author after H.C Andersen and the Grimm brothers.

Right: Astrid Lindgren with Inger Nilsson as Pippi Longstocking in the 1969 TV series

Below: One of illustrator Jenny Nyström's ever popular Christmas images

The atmospheric island of Stora Karlsö,
6.5 kilometres southwest of Gotland. The
lighthouse is just visible in the distance

The giant Rauks or natural limestone pillars of Fårö island. Famous film director, Ingmar Bergman lived and died here, his cinematographic legacy perpetuated through the Bergman Foundation

ISLANDS APART, AGRICULTURE AT HEART

Distinct in character from the mainland with their unique and rugged landscapes, the islands of Öland and Gotland have held a magnetic pull on human visitors for thousands of years. Historically, the limestone rich soil has also been a challenge for those attempting to live there, a fact recognised by UNESCO, which declared the southern part of Öland a World Heritage site in 2000, serving as an outstanding example of human settlement, making optimal usage of diverse landscape types on a single island. It is this agricultural resourcefulness that has inspired innovation in recent times, for example in the Moving Floor Concept, a fully automatic system of removing animal manure and refilling hay/straw designed by Tommy Lindvall, a Gotland farmer. The concept, which was first exported in 2009, has been patented to include systems for calves, pigs, horses and more.

Above right: The ruins of Borgholm castle, Öland

Right: The Moving Floor concept

The Hanseatic town of Visby is a UNESCO World Heritage site

THE ISLANDS IN A NUTSHELL

Öland total population: 24 987
Largest towns: Mörbylånga (14 368),
Borgholm (10 619)

Did you know? Öland is the favoured setting for novels by acclaimed Swedish writer Johan Teorin (Echoes from the dead). The Öland bridge, linking Kalmar on the mainland to Färjestad on the island, is one of the longest in Europe.

How to get here: By bridge or ferry from Kalmar.

Gotland total population: 57 161
Largest town: Visby (22 500)

Did you know? Visby has an illustrious history. It is the birthplace of Christopher Polhem – the 'Father of Swedish mechanics' and living ice-hockey legend, Håkan Loob.

How to get here: Ferry from Nynäshamn (Stockholm), Oskarshamn or fly to Visby from Stockholm, Gothenburg or Malmö.

SMÅLAND IN A NUTSHELL

Counties: Jönköping, Kronoberg, Kalmar
Total Population: 762 265
Three largest towns: Jönköping (130 798),
Växjö (85 822), Kalmar (63 887)

Did you know? Other famous names from Småland include the great 20th Century author, Vilhelm Moberg (The Emigrants series) and smash-hit composer and musician, Björn Ulvaeus (Abba).

How to get here: Fly into Jönköping or Kalmar airports from Stockholm in less than an hour or drive/take the train for a more leisurely five-hour tour down south. Kalmar marina is a welcoming haven for sailors too!

East Middle Sweden

SKY-HIGH AMBITION, FINGER ON THE PULSE

You can almost sense a breeze of achievement rippling the surface of the Göta Canal, that 19th Century feat of engineering that created a continuous water way from Gothenburg in the west to Söderköping in the east. Although the advent of railway would soon nullify any of the canal's logistical advantages, it was an inspired endeavour that sent waves of innovation downstream, establishing centres of technical expertise along its banks and beyond.

Let's take a towpath tour…

THE MIDDLE OF NO-WHERE GETS SOMEWHERE

A diminutive village for centuries, and still a small town today, Motala became the capital of the Göta Canal, thanks to Motala Verkstad, established in 1822. Initially set up to manufacture parts for the construction of the canal, the company later grew in skill and stature, going on to build some 400 ships, 800 bridges and 1,300 locomotives. It retains its international reputation today in the manufacture of specialised medical, maritime and industrial equipment.

Above left: Cruising gently down the Göta canal

Above right: Statesman Baltzar von Platen oversaw the construction of the Göta Canal and founded Motala Verkstad. The locomotive shown here was built in 1862

UP, UP AND AWAY

Continuing east to Lake Roxen, we approach Linköping, which was just another small town until 1937, when the founding of Saab gave it soaring aspirations. Since then, fighter jets such as the Lansen, Draken, Viggen and all manner of aeronautical, missile and defence systems have been rolled out here. The latest fighter, JAS Gripen, forms the backbone air defence of five countries, and incorporates fantasy-like features such as Super Sensor Fusion and Fly-By-Wire Flight Control.

Linköping has grown into an important university town and centre for high-tech industry

WINNING THE WORLD OVER, ONE DEGREE AT A TIME

Deviating off the tow path now and heading north, our next stop is Uppsala, where learning and great innovations have gone hand in hand for centuries. Most famous of these is perhaps Anders Celsius' temperature scale, without which water would not freeze at 0 or boil at 100. Other Uppsala-educated greats of Celsius' era include Emmanuel Swedenborg, Torbern Bergman and Carl Von Linné – all extremely influential in shaping the world of science as we know it.

Above left: Emmanuel Swedenborg (1688-1772) came up with detailed designs for a submarine and an airplane

Above right: Torbern Bergman (1735-1784) is acknowledged as the founder of modern chemistry in Sweden. His apparatus for carbonating water laid the foundation for Swedish mineral water manufacture and was a first step towards the soft drinks industry of today

Established in 1477, Uppsala University was the first university in Sweden

The natural harbour of Gubbö in the Östergötland archipelago

Lake Bolen, in Norrköping municipality. In winter, many frozen lakes in the area are ploughed for long distance skating or cross country skiing

The safety match – Gustaf Erik Pasch (1788-1862) born in Norrköping

Matches are a very old invention but the white phosphorous used to make them was highly toxic and prone to accidental combustion. In 1844, Swedish chemist Pasch patented and started producing matchsticks using non-toxic red phosphorous on the striking surface. However, various technical difficulties dashed any hopes of commercial success, and it was not until 1853 that the safety match was born – the result of improvements made by Carl and Johan Lundström at their matchstick factory in Jönköping. It was a lucky strike indeed, as by 1896 they were making more than 7 million boxes of matches a year and the rest is world history.

The adjustable spanner – Johan Petter Johansson (1853-1943) est. Enköpings Mekaniska Verkstad

Although designs from England and the USA had been emerging around the same time, it was Johansson's spanner that set the standard we know and love. Having set up business in Enköping, Johansson clinched the deal of a life time in 1890, when his tools were distributed worldwide under the Bahco trademark. Still in operation today, Bahco tools have manufactured over 100 million spanners to date.

The rollator – Aina Lucia Wifalk
(1928-1983) hospital welfare officer, Västerås

Having suffered from polio at the age of 21, Aina Wifalk had been dependent on crutches for almost a quarter of a century before coming up with her brilliant mobility solution in 1978. Its potential was recognised by a government development fund and three years later, the rollator went into production. Wanting her invention to benefit as many as possible, Wifalk never sought a patent. It is thanks to this generous gesture that millions of people with walking difficulties now enjoy greater freedom of movement.

EAST MIDDLE SWEDEN
IN A NUTSHELL

Counties: Östergötland, Örebro, Södermanland, Västmanland, Uppsala
Total Population: 1 605 347
Three largest cities: Uppsala (205 199), Linköping (150 202), Västerås (142 131)

Did you know? East Middle Sweden has nurtured a number of internationally acclaimed rock bands, including Lolita Pop (Örebro), Louise Hoffsten (Linköping) and Kent (Eskilstuna).

How to get here: All three major cities have good rail and air links. Uppsala is just 36 km north of Stockholm Arlanda, while Linköping and Västerås have their own airports.

Stockholm

SUSTAINABLE CAPITAL, HARD-WIRED FOR THE FUTURE

The olde worlde charm of Gamla Stan may fool us into thinking Stockholm is all about the quaint and historic, but nowhere embodies the Swedes' passion for new technology quite like the capital. Having embraced modernism in the 20th Century, Swedes have had little trouble embracing IT in the 21st. And it is this forward-thinking that has led to Sweden ranking among the most digitally connected economies in the world.

So, how hard-wired are they?

FROM MICRO-IP TO MINECRAFT

You're on your way to the airport and forgotten to turn off the heating at home. Perhaps you're in the grocery store and want to check what's in your fridge. Solving these problems remotely with a smart phone is now possible thanks to Micro IP, devised by Swedish programmer, Adam Dunkels in 2007. But if you're sceptical about such long distance wizardry, think again – Ericsson predict that 50 billion devices will be wirelessly connected by 2020. The Age of the Internet of Things has begun!

Less time spent solving domestic issues means more time for… computer games. Someone who knows this better than anyone is Markus 'Notch' Persson, the creator of mega-buster building sim Minecraft, which has sold more than 50 million copies across platforms since its official launch in 2011. Persson hit the jackpot in September 2014, however, when Microsoft snapped up his Stockholm games studio, Mojang for a bright and breezy USD 2.5 billion.

The appeal of Minecraft is its creative scope. Players are allowed to build anything they please with the resources they choose. Avoiding monsters comes into it, of course!

Micro IP requires very little code and RAM – perfect for small, low powered devices, such as this remote-controlled, multi-coloured light bulb

Scenic Söder Mälarstrand, with some of its permanently docked boats

BEEN THERE, DONE THAT

The last decade has seen nothing short of a revolution in terms of connective capabilities. We are integrating new services into our lives so fast we hardly remember what it was like before they existed. Some of the Stockholm-born innovations we now take for granted:

4G

The 3G networks that first enabled true mobile internet access are now being superseded by LTE, the technology behind 4G. Closely involved in its development are the much applauded Ericsson team, who were finalists in the 2014 European Inventor Award. Although the super-fast network is still not ubiquitous, Swedish Telia Sonera began offering 4G services to its Scandinavian customers as early as December 2009.

Skype

Founded in 2003 by Swede Niklas Zennström and Dane Janus Friis, Skype took the 'ouch' out of overseas call costs for millions of people. With free voice and video calls over the internet, Skype was so revolutionary in its inception that eBay acquired it in 2005, only for Microsoft to reel it in for USD 8.5 billion in 2011.

Spotify

Legally streaming and sharing copyrighted music online, the Spotify alternative to pirated music file-sharing sites has taken the world by storm. When Daniel Ek and Martin Lorentzon launched the company in 2008, they could not have envisaged having 40 million users around the globe by 2014.

EXPLOSIVE IDEAS FOR EVERY ERA

Swedish inventors have contributed to human progress through every era, but two of the most notable in the last 150 years are:

Alfred Nobel 1833-1896

During his lifetime, Nobel patented as many as 355 inventions, the most world-changing of these being dynamite. Nobel had been surrounded by explosives and danger from the start – first selling matchsticks as a child and then working at his father's munitions works in St Petersburg. Having succeeded in stabilising nitro-glycerine in the form of dynamite in 1867, Alfred went on to invent blasting gelatine (more explosive than dynamite and could be used under water) and ballistite, which did not produce smoke when it exploded. Originally intended for use in the construction industry, these inventions were soon put to devastating use in the course of war. Realising the full impact of his work towards the end of his life, Nobel came up with perhaps his greatest invention – the Nobel Prizes – a legacy of peaceful endeavour for generations to come.

Left: Selma Lagerlöf, winner of the Nobel Prize for Literature in 1909

Right: Alfred Nobel, inventor extraordinaire

Håkan Lans 1947-

Happier constructing motorised model vehicles than going for the grade at school, Håkan Lans first came to the world's attention in 1968, when he succeeded in making a mini submarine that could descend to a depth of 90 metres. However, his real fame came while working as a research assistant at the Swedish Defence Research establishment, FOA, where he developed Datacolor, a colour graphics processor. Here he also invented the 'digitizer' – a precursor to the modern computer mouse. Lans' greatest invention has nevertheless been the STDMA navigation system, which combines both GPS and radio. Patented in the mid-1990s, the system was quickly adopted by the shipping industry, but it was not until 2004 that it also became a world standard for aviation.

Glasbrukssjön, Nacka,
Stockholm county

Hammarby, south Stockholm. The area is known for its sports club and new, popular residential areas, such as Hammarby Sjöstad

HOME SWEET HOME

If there is one defining characteristic of the Swedes, it is their love of the home. Having invented some of the most essential pieces of household equipment, they have gone on to take our expectations of domestic bliss to new heights.

The refrigerator

Baltzar von Platen and Carl Munters were two young students at the Royal Institute of Technology in Stockholm when they presented their refrigerator to the world in 1922. Revolutionising food management in the home, von Platen and Munters' invention kick-started their careers with Electrolux, and was one of the reasons for the rapid expansion of the company.

Left: Baltzar von Platen and Carl Munters

The water-cooled D-fridge from 1925 – the first refrigerator to be produced by Electrolux

The classic lines of Electrolux refrigerators from the 1940s

The Aga

Gustaf Dalén had already won the Nobel Prize in Physics for his work with gas accumulators and lighthouse illumination in 1912, but it was his AGA cooker that won the hearts of homemakers, a decade later. Upon discovering that his wife was exhausted from cooking chores, Dalén developed a new smoke-free and efficient stove which worked on the principle of heat storage. The AGA's enduring appeal has made it a must-have for kitchen aficionados to this day.

The iconic AGA stove, as popular as ever

The vacuum cleaner

Although Electrolux wasn't first on the market with home vacuum cleaners, their 1921 Model V set the standard for generations of future machines. In 2001, they set the standard again with Inese Ljunggren's Trilobite, the world's first robot vacuum cleaner. Programmable and equipped with an infra-red sensor, the arthropod-inspired machine can navigate its way round your home with ease, picking up dust and dirt while you go out and have fun.

The Trilobite, the world's first robotic vacuum cleaner

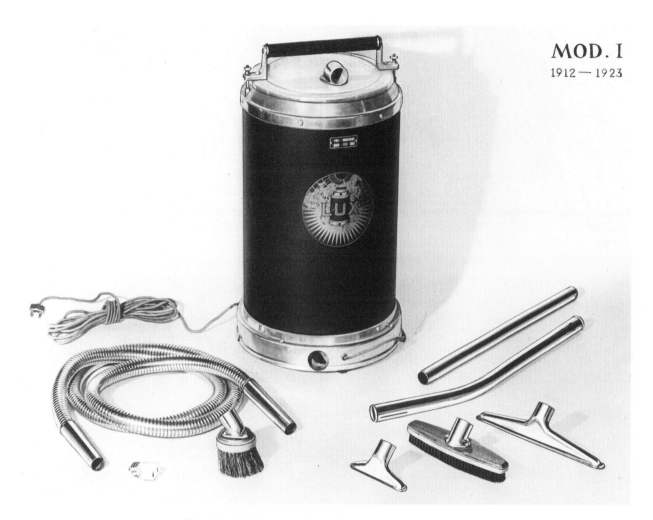

The Model I Lux, produced from 1912-1923

STOCKHOLM
IN A NUTSHELL

Counties: Stockholm city and environs
Total Population: 2 163 042

Did you know? Two greats of the silver screen, Greta Garbo and Ingrid Bergman were both born in the capital. Stockholmers who have made it big in Hollywood more recently include Stellan Skarsgård and son Alexander Skarsgård.

How to get here: With over a million visitors each year, Stockholm has to be well connected. Two international airports, Arlanda and Bromma take care of the air traffic, while an ample network of trains and buses bring people into the heart of the city. On a cruise and fancy a stop off? Whether you're travelling by ocean liner or dingy, you'll find safe harbour.

North Middle Sweden

TIMBERTASTIC, OOZING WITH TRADITION

Fresh, sweet pine forests – these have been a treasure trove for centuries of Swedes, not least those living in the northern, inland parts of the country. But what if all those generations of lumberjacks, berry gatherers and bark bread makers woke up one day to be told the fruits of the forest were now textiles, plastics and fibre optics?

As amazing as it may seem, the timber-rich counties of Värmland, Dalarna and Gävleborg could soon wake up to just that, and see their forests as an exciting source of renewable, bio-based materials that will catapult us into a new era of smart, sustainable living.

LIGNIN NOT LINGUINE

Versatile, tough and renewable, wood-derived lignin is about to become a heavyweight on the materials market. Swedish research group Innventia has already succeeded in using the polymer to produce carbon fibre, and is working to make it a commercially viable alternative to the petroleum-derived material by 2025.

Upper right: Pine oil derivatives are already being used in Swedish Preem's Evolution diesel, a world first containing up to 35% renewables and cutting CO2 emissions by up to 31%. Their next step in moving away from fossil fuels is to use lignin to make bio petrol

Right: Formula 1, satellites, technically advanced sports gear... When high performance and low weight are non-negotiable, carbon fibre is the go-to material. But lignin-based products will transform the industry, making cheaper grades of carbon fibre available for wider applications

Crystalline nanocellulose – the fibre optic of the future?

NANO NANO

No, it's not from outer space, it's from inner wood: nanocellulose, another renewable forestry product that is stepping up as a super material. As strong as Kevlar, and with all the versatility of plastic, nanocellulose has vast fields of application. Until now, the high energy cost of production ruled out commercialisation but Swedish Innventia has successfully cut this by 98%, making nanocellulose hot news once more.

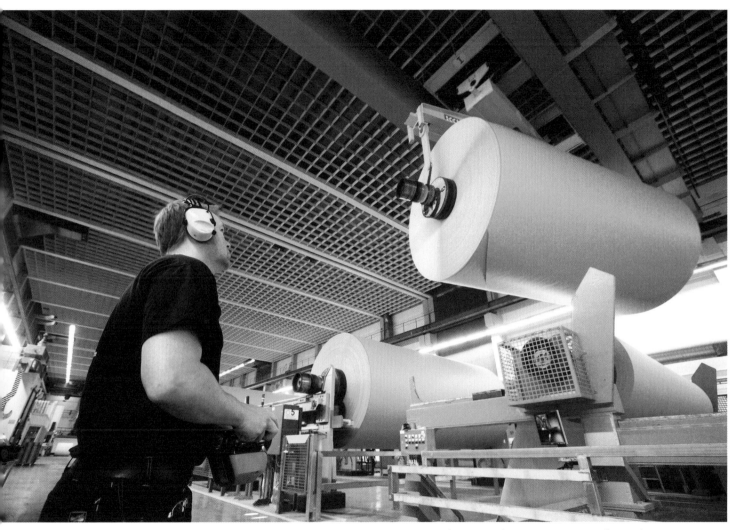

BillerudKorsnäs. Originally humble saw and paper mills, Billerud AB (Värmland) and Korsnäs AB (Gävle) have become forest industry giants, and finally merged in 2012. While paper pulp and timber were their bread and butter last century, lignin and nanocellulose could become their staples in the 21ˢᵗ

UNESCO world heritage site, Stora Kopparberget, Falun, The copper mine was one of North Middle Sweden's greatest mineral assets for centuries

VISION 2035

Can't quite imagine a world with biomaterials? Fortunately, the Swedish forest industry has devised an inspirational conceptual model to help us understand their future potential. A few highlights from www.ekoportal2035.se:

Organicglass
Crystalline material from nanocellulose and lignocellulose that has much more flexibility than ordinary glass, meaning it can be made into things like large convex windows without difficulty.

FoamWater
A completely biodegradable product that transforms just 1 litre of water into many litres of Foam-Water – perfect for showers in households that must keep water consumption to a minimum.

Celloran
A cellulose based textile that feels like a mixture of silk and Egyptian cotton. Apart from its appealing comfort, it has dirt repellent and antibacterial properties and can be embedded with sensors to make a hi-tech textile that can be used in hospitals, for example, to monitor changes in a patient's biological status.

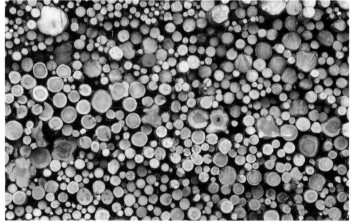

The home of Carl and Karin Larsson, Dalarna's most famous artistic couple of the 20th Century. The cultural heritage and folk traditions of this region are recognised worldwide as symbols of Sweden as a whole

LOCAL GENIUS, GLOBAL SUCCESS

Of course, forestry isn't the only source of innovation in North Middle Sweden. True to form, inventors from this part of the country have been coming up with practical solutions to some of life's most fundamental problems. Two modern innovations that are fast becoming essential pieces of equipment around the world:

QuickSave

Would you struggle to dive in and pull a submerged adult to safety from a depth of 4 metres? Åsa Magnusson from Falun had this problem in mind when she devised her pocket-sized life buoy that inflates under water. Having won the European award for women inventors, EUWIIN in 2011, Åsa has gone on to develop a range of life-saving equipment that is now used by firefighters, life guards and other professional rescuers in many countries.

Noaq

Flooding due to climate-change is increasingly a homeowner's headache – and a hole in their wallet. But what if you could stop the flow of water in its tracks and prop it up like a book-end? Sigurd Melin from Näsviken did just that with Noaq, a flood protection system of interconnected inflatable tubes that creates a water barrier. Noaq won the BBC 'Best Inventions' award in 2002 and is the fastest, lightest, most flexible flood protection system on the market today.

THE CURIOUS CASE OF NINNI KRONBERG

In the 1930s Sweden was producing too much milk – what to do before it all turned sour? In 1933, nutritionist Ninni Kronberg from Gävle came up with the answer, finding a way to make dry milk powder from the surplus. Although Ninni took patents for her discovery in Sweden, Canada and the USA, it was not until financier Axel Wenner-Gren started the Semper dry milk factory in 1939 that her product went global, providing a life line to countries where milk was in short supply. Strangely enough, little is known about the woman behind this ground-breaking discovery, yet generations of babies around the world have Ninni to thank for her inspired invention.

NORTH MIDDLE SWEDEN
IN A NUTSHELL

Counties: Värmland, Dalarna, Gävleborg
Total Population: 829 134
Three largest cities: Gävle (97 236),
Karlstad (87 786), Falun (56 767)

*Did you know? Vasaloppet, the oldest, longest
and biggest cross-country skiing race in the
world is held between the towns of Sälen and
Mora in Dalarna. Around 15 000 people partici-
pate each year in the gruelling 90 km challenge.*

How to get here: Karlstad airport in Värmland handles flights to international charter destinations
as well as scheduled flights to Stockholm and
Frankfurt. As an important tourist centre, Dalarna
has two airports handling domestic flights, one in
Borlänge and one in Mora, and a good train ser-
vice operates throughout the region as a whole.

Middle Norrland

WINTER WONDERLAND, SPORTING EXCELLENCE

Charlotte Kalla, Johan Olsson and Anna Holmlund – these are just three of the fifteen Swedes who brought home medals from the 2014 Winter Olympics. Although hard graft, talent and determination were fundamental to their success, that little je ne sais quoi that helped them rise above the competition may just have something to do with where they train: in Norrland.

Åre, Sweden's most popular ski resort

Not only is this region Sweden's favourite alpine playground, it is also home to one of the world's leading centres for physiological and medicinal research in the field of winter sports. And while research here aims to help elite sportsmen and women improve every aspect of their performance, it has also stumbled upon some exciting findings with much wider applications.

An athlete undergoing tests, Östersund. Facilities at the Swedish Winter Sports Research Centre include sophisticated tools such as iDXA body scanning, isokinetic testing and 3D film to analyse body profiles and help identify performance weaknesses

APRÈS SKI, IT'S TIME FOR 3D

Mention 3D-printing or additive manufacture, and most tech-savvy individuals will nod excitedly in recognition of this revolutionary process, which creates objects of almost any shape from a digital model. In experimenting to make things like optimally ergonomic ski pole handles and new bindings, the Sportstech research group at Mid Sweden University soon realised their work could have more thrilling applications: in medicine. Ten years ago, the team started collaborating with Östersund hospital to make plastic 3D models of complicated fractures, helping surgeons prepare for operations and design custom-fit implants in an entirely new way. Having moved on to creating actual implants in metals such as titanium, Sportstech were the first lab in the world to test the use of iron-based, amorphous metal in 2012. This introduces a whole new ball game of future possibilities, including the additive manufacture of products with inbuilt functionality.

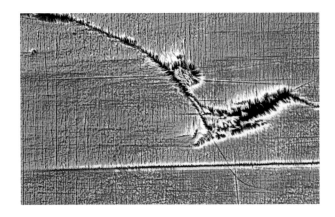

Amorphous metal is more elastic and many times stronger than metal with ordinary atomic structure, meaning implants can be made to a perfect fit and almost infinite lifespan

ARCTIC FOX MAKES BACKPACKING A BREEZE

Needless to say, simply exploring the great outdoors was popular with Norrlanders long before the region gained its reputation for elite winter sports training. Back in 1950, fourteen year-old Åke Nordin from Örnsköldsvik had a thing about back packs. Keen to trek in the mountains but not so keen on the awkward and uncomfortable rucksacks available at the time, Åke set about making his own – with a wooden frame that positioned the weight high up, distributing the load much better across the back. By 1960, Åke had his company Fjällräven (Arctic fox) up and running from the family's home. The workshop was in the cellar, and here the first backpacks with aluminium frames were created, as well as things like condensation-free lightweight tents, functional outdoor clothing and revolutionary sleeping bags, which would come to be loved by outdoor enthusiasts everywhere.

Arctic fox, wolverine and lynx are some of the more exotic creatures you may be lucky enough to spot roaming the Norrland countryside

KÅNKEN

Lightweight and durable, Kånken was launched in 1978 to help prevent back problems in school children. Over thirty-five years on, the backpack has become a Fjällräven classic and enjoys retro-cool status around the world.

Above: A young Åke Nordin with the rucksack he designed and made

Above left: The basement workshop where Fjällräven began. Today, their products are sold in more than 20 countries

The gorgeous countryside of Norrfällsviken,
Kramfors municipality

ODDBALL IDEAS TO MAKE YOUR TASTE BUDS TINGLE

Caramelised cheese or rotten herrings, anyone? Both of these weird and wonderful foods have long been part of Norrland's culinary heritage. Look out for:

Fjällbrynt messmör/mesost

The Fjällbrynt company in Östersund has been making this unusual, sweet-tasting dairy product since 1939. Milk, cream and whey are boiled together until the water evaporates and the heat turns the milk sugar into caramel. Messmör is the resulting sweet brown 'butter' or, if left to boil longer, mesost – a firmer brown cheese.

Röda Ulven surströmming

Pungent, gassy and tongue-curling, fermented Baltic herring never fails to make an impression. In 2006, several airlines even banned the fish from their carriers, classifying it along with dangerous weapons like shoe bombs and firearms. But in the surströmming heartlands of Höga Kusten you can be sure to see (or at least smell) many a happy herring party in late August, when this delicacy has its seasonal premiere.

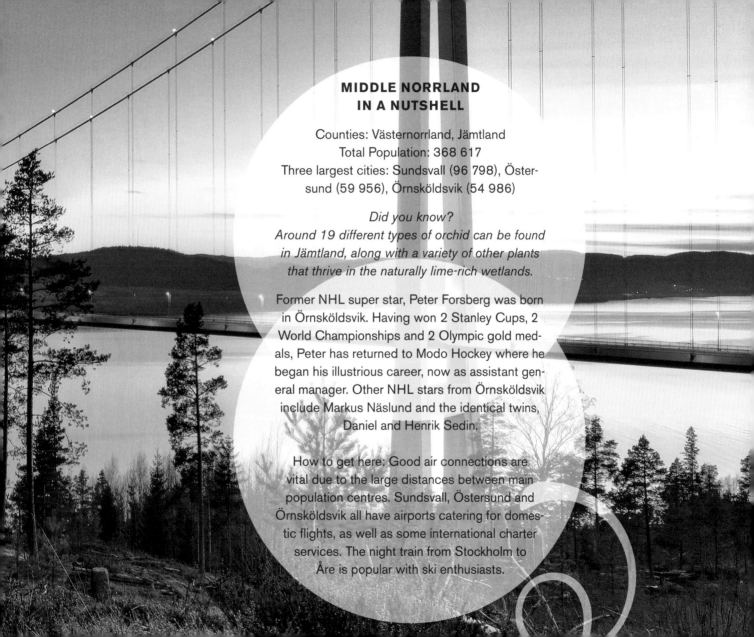

MIDDLE NORRLAND
IN A NUTSHELL

Counties: Västernorrland, Jämtland
Total Population: 368 617
Three largest cities: Sundsvall (96 798), Öster-
sund (59 956), Örnsköldsvik (54 986)

Did you know?
Around 19 different types of orchid can be found
in Jämtland, along with a variety of other plants
that thrive in the naturally lime-rich wetlands.

Former NHL super star, Peter Forsberg was born
in Örnsköldsvik. Having won 2 Stanley Cups, 2
World Championships and 2 Olympic gold medals, Peter has returned to Modo Hockey where he
began his illustrious career, now as assistant general manager. Other NHL stars from Örnsköldsvik
include Markus Näslund and the identical twins,
Daniel and Henrik Sedin.

How to get here: Good air connections are
vital due to the large distances between main
population centres. Sundsvall, Östersund and
Örnsköldsvik all have airports catering for domestic flights, as well as some international charter
services. The night train from Stockholm to
Åre is popular with ski enthusiasts.

Upper Norrland

NOMADIC NATURE, SPACE-AGE THINKING

Take a helicopter tour over the wild expanses of Sweden's northernmost territories and you'll see a landscape on the move: reindeer, people – a city even, as Kiruna embarks on the first phase of its long-anticipated transformation.

Indeed, movement and transformation characterise both the indigenous peoples dwelling in these remote parts, and the brave newcomers drawn here to explore the wonders of the wilderness – or the sky above it.

Kiruna – a town on the move. The magnetite in this area is among the richest iron ore deposits in the world and LKAB have been mining here since the beginning of the 1900s. As mining operations have caused land deformation at the town's boundaries, Kiruna town centre is being relocated 3 km east of the existing one. A new railway, roads, new housing, shops – in fact every aspect of infrastructure is being re-jigged to create an all new and exciting Kiruna!

Kiruna space station

IS IT A BIRD, IS IT A PLANE...?

No, it's Cryosat – just one of the European Space Agency's satellites supported by the Kiruna space station. Situated at Salmijärvi, 38 km east of Kiruna, the station's high-latitude position makes it ideal for tracking low Earth orbiting satellites as it provides visibility for 10-12 out of 14 daily orbits. So, what's going on up there?

ESA Cryosat launched in 2010, Cryosat's main mission is to monitor variations in the thickness of polar sea ice, giving critical feedback about sea levels and climate change. Cryosat has surpassed expectations in terms of its ability to profile not only ice thickness, but also small, local phenomena in ocean surfaces, giving far greater accuracy in forecasting storm surges, for example.

EISCAT Whether it's close encounters with asteroids or satellite collisions with space junk – SSA, or Space Situational Awareness is of increasing global importance due to threats from dangerous debris in the Earth's orbit. The EISCAT sensor facilities in Kiruna track rogue objects, helping to detect their re-entry into the atmosphere, and assist in the prediction and warning of collision – potentially saving lives, homes and national infrastructure in the process.

ESA Swarm trio, Integral Two more important satellite missions: Swarm monitoring Earth's changing magnetism and Integral observing some of the most violent events in space, including gamma ray bursts and black holes.

Luleå Gammelstad UNESCO world heritage site

The Facebook data centre at Luleå University Campus went online in 2012. A second data centre on the same site is on its way

CHILL OUT OR REV IT UP

With winter temperatures averaging well in excess of −10° C across the region, it can feel like one giant freezer for almost six months of the year. And although that thought might send shivers down your spine, these sub-zero conditions do have their advantages...

The Node Pole

A cluster of municipalities is rapidly making a name for itself in high tech, electricity intensive construction. Free cooling for at least 8-10 months of the year and reliable, low-priced electricity from 100% renewable hydropower make the Luleå-Boden-Piteå triangle perfect for data centres – hence the name 'The Node Pole'. Sweden's political and geological stability, along with extremely high technological readiness and broadband connectivity are two further factors attracting big business: Facebook is so happy with its data centre in Luleå, they're constructing another one!

Vehicle testing

ABS, Anti-skid systems, tyre performance... the European hub of winter car testing is to be found in sparsely populated Arjeplog, just 100 km south of the Arctic Circle. Thick ice on the extensive system of lakes in the area are the ideal brakes testing ground, while kilometres of purpose-built forest tracks provide rigorous conditions – and private space – to put new cars through their paces, away from prying eyes. Bosch, BMW and Mercedes are among the big brands who test here.

Above: The vehicle testing industry here has grown massively since its start in the 1970s. There are less than 0.5 people per square kilometre in these parts – although the population doubles in winter, when 3,000 car testers descend on Arjeplog

Umeå Arts Campus, which brings the Umeå School of Architecture, Institute of Design and Academy of Fine Arts together in one creative hub

AWARD-WINNING SCIENCE UP NORTH

Umeå has established itself as a science mecca, with over 3 000 people employed in life science companies and academia. The areas it excels in include infectious disease research, diagnostic and medical technology and plant and forest biotechnology. Two examples:

Bacteria

Emmanuelle Charpentier, from Umeå University has been awarded The Breakthrough Prize in Life Sciences 2015. The prize brings attention to research endeavouring to find cures for serious diseases. Charpentier shares her prize with Jennifer Doudna, University of California, Berkeley, 'for harnessing an ancient mechanism of bacterial immunity into a powerful and general technology for editing genomes, with wide-reaching implications across biology and medicine'.

Blood clots

On Deloitte's list of the fastest growing tech companies in Sweden is Nordic Biomarker, a successful Umeå based company that manufactures reagents for diagnostic testing of clotting, or deep venous thrombosis. Founded in 2007, when one of their future customers begged them to start manufacturing reagents for them, Nordic Biomarker tests are now used all over the world to diagnose blood clots and potentially save lives.

A distant view of Abisko Scientific Research Station, against the magnificent backdrop of the Lapponian Gate. Natural science research and meteorological observations have been conducted in this area since the early 1900s. The station plays an important role in international climate research, attracting researchers from around the world

The rapids of Vindelälven. The river runs from the border with Norway in the southern part of Arjeplog municipality and joins the Umeälven river just inland from Umeå, on the Baltic coast. With its high biodiversity, the Vindelälven region is a strong contender for status as a UNESCO biosphere reserve, the aim of which is to exemplify sustainable development benefiting both humans and the environment.

Bringing in the herd. Of the approximately 20 000 Sámi who live in Sweden, only 2 500 are active in reindeer husbandry

At 35 km long, Rapadalen is the largest valley in Sarek National Park

UPPER NORRLAND
IN A NUTSHELL

Counties: Västerbotten, Norrbotten
Total Population: 510 548
Three largest cities: Umeå (118 349),
Luleå (75 383), Skellefteå (71 988)

Did you know? Västerbotten cheese, which has been produced in Burträsk since 1872, is a favourite accompaniment at Swedish crayfish parties in August. The tangy, hard cheese with tiny holes now enjoys an international reputation, and you can even buy it in the British supermarket Waitrose.

How to get here: All the main centres, including Kiruna have air links with Stockholm and other Swedish cities. Fancy a trip to Lapland? From London Stanstead you can fly directly to Skellefteå, which is just a 1½ hour bus or car journey from Arvidsjaur. As well as domestic flights, Arvidsjaur airport also handles direct flights to four cities in Germany.

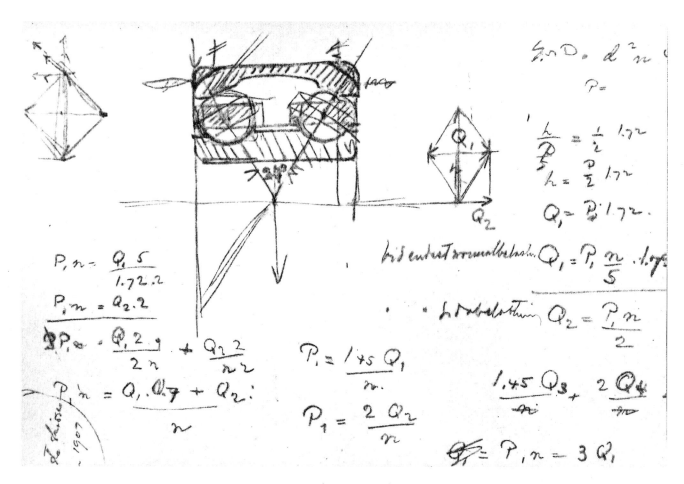

An early sketch by Sven Wingquist (1876-1953) of his double-row, self-aligning ball bearing. Patented in 1907, the revolutionary design would be the catalyst for SKF's rapid expansion as an international ball bearing manufacturer

Just amazing...
innovation pick and mix

Whether it's steam turbines or armoured warships, zips or Coca-Coca bottles, you can be sure Swedes have been in on the action through every era of innovation. While some inventions dazzle with their technical brilliance, others dazzle in their simplicity. Are you thinking 'Wow factor' or 'Why didn't I think of that?' Find your favourite in this just amazing pick and mix!

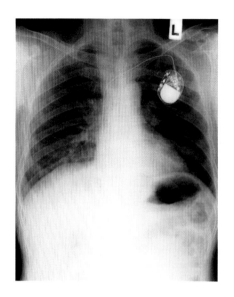

TICKETY TOCK

In 1958, Arne Larsson became the world's
first patient to receive a fully implantable
cardiac pacemaker at Karolinska Institutet in
Stockholm. Larsson went on to receive 26
different pacemakers in his lifetime and died
at age 86, outliving both the inventor of the
pacemaker (Rune Elmqvist) and the surgeon
(Åke Senning) who performed the operation.

MOONING AROUND

Now the most famous name in cameras, Gothen-burg-based Victor Hasselblad only really took off in 1962, when NASA randomly selected the 500 C as the first camera to be sent to space. Amazed by the fantastic pictures, NASA continued it collabora-tion with Hasselblad, their most pivotal mission be-ing Apollo 11 in 1969, when Neil Armstrong used the 500 EDC on his momentous moon walk.

NOT TO BE SNIFFED AT...

With 2.5 billion people still lacking basic sanitation, affordable, sustainable solutions are a global concern. In 2005, Swedish Professor Anders Wilhelmson invented the Peepoo, a fully biodegradable, single-use toilet that inactivates dangerous pathogens and serves as a completely harmless fertiliser after use. Currently employed in the Kibera slum, Kenya and humanitarian disaster responses worldwide.

SUN-KISSED SOLUTION

Saving lives has been Solvatten's business
since 2006, its patented, portable water
treatment unit allowing households to heat
up and treat contaminated water using
solar energy. Petra Wadström came up with
the idea while living in Australia in 1997;
now she is CEO to a company that is helping to make clean water accessible to all.

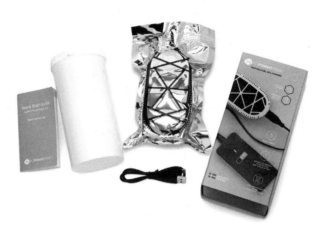

PLENTY OF JUICE

A tablespoon of water to charge your mobile? With MyFC's PowerTrekk, that's all it takes. Invented and developed by researcher Anders Lundblad, the charger uses ordinary water and salt to power a fuel cell, making it the perfect energy solution when plugging in is not an option. PowerTrekk was first released in 2012 and now sells in over 24 countries.

GO FOR THE BURN

Carl Richard Nyberg made a fortune from his invention of the blow torch, after conceiving the idea as a metal worker and joining forces with industrialist Max Sievert in 1882. Employing a new vaporising technique for liquid fuel, Nyberg's torch was quickly adopted by other manufacturers and is still the blue print design for similar torches used today.

WHEN THE CHIPS ARE DOWN

In 1748, 25-year-old Eva de la Gardie became
the first woman to be elected into the Royal
Swedish Academy of Sciences for discovering
a method of making aquavit from potatoes. This
was important at the time, as it meant Sweden
could save grain to make bread rather than its
favourite tipple. Eva's scientific contributions also
included a method of bleaching textiles with soap,
and a non-toxic potato powder alternative to the
arsenic-laden cosmetics of the day.

GREEN GLOOP GOES LARGE

A new strain of microalgae found by two Gothenburg researchers on a polar expedition in 2012 is set to become big news as a biofuel. The algae, which has the astonishing ability to grow in extremely low light conditions, can be exploited both as a renewable source of crude oil and as an industrial waste water treatment. Discoverers of the algae and inventors of the process, Swedish Algae Factory won the Swedish finals in the 2014 Venture Cup Environment and Energy category, and are aiming to become the leading biofuel company in Europe by 2030.

GET A GRIP

Bioservo Technologies' SEM glove is winning hands down in helping people who lack strength and grip due to conditions such as stroke and arthritis, or for other reasons. The soft robotic glove, which mimics human anatomy through finger sensors and artificial tendons, carried off the international Robotdalen Innovation Award in 2012 and is rapidly gaining a reputation on the international market.

GYNIUS FOR DETAIL

Wanting to make cervical examinations convenient and accessible to women in all kinds of health settings, gynaecologist Elisabeth Wikström Shemer invented the Gynocular – the world's first truly portable colposcope. Through her company Gynius AB, the pocket-sized microscope is being distributed worldwide, and a buy and donate programme further facilitates access to this vital piece of equipment.

ANITA SHENOI

Fascinated by all things Scandinavian and blond, Anita Shenoi moved from urban Britain to the wilds of Sweden as a student and has continued to explore the Nordic way of life ever since. Having lived in Stockholm for a number of years, Anita now divides her time between Sweden and the UK, working as a writer and translator.

PHOTOGRAPHS

All other photographs: Shutterstock